Thea King and Alan Frank

Schumann for the Clarinet

Eleven songs arranged for B flat clarinet and piano

The Associated Board of the Royal Schools of Music

PREFACE

Robert Schumann (1810-1856) wrote about 250 songs for voice and piano.
They form an outstanding part of his output and have few rivals in the
history of song. They are essentially *duets* for voice and piano – rather
than songs with piano accompaniment – and this must be reflected in
playing the present arrangements. The clarinettist must listen intently
to the piano part, and must shade and vary the playing accordingly.
The same, obviously, applies to the pianist in performing what we hope
is a playable distillation of Schumann's originals.

The pieces are arranged roughly in order of the clarinet part's technical
difficulty. The speeds at which they are played need not follow the speeds
of the original songs: in one case (No.9), it is much slower than it is
usually sung.

Finally we wish to acknowledge the assistance of David Bray in his role
as amanuensis – and often more than that.

T.K./A.F.

CONTENTS

		piano	*part*
1	'You are like a flower' (*Du bist wie eine Blume*), Op.25 No.24	*page* 4	*page* 1
2	A Greeting (*Widmung*), Op.25 No.1	6	2
3	Folksong (*Volksliedchen*), Op.51 No.2	10	3
4	Lotus flower (*Die Lotosblume*), Op.25 No.7	12	4
5	'Ring on my finger' (*Du Ring an meinem Finger*'), Op.42 No.4	14	5
6	'My heart's in the highlands' (*Hochländers Abschied*), Op.25 No.13	17	6
7	Noblest of Men ('*Er, der Herrlichste von Allen*'), Op.42 No.2	19	6
8	The Two Grenadiers (*Die beiden Grenadiere*), Op.49 No.1	24	8
9	May Song ('*Im wunderschönen Monat Mai*'), Op.48 No.1	28	9
10	A Song for Sunday (*Sonntag*), Op.79 No.6	30	10
11	Grandee of Spain (*Der Hidalgo*), Op.30 No.3	32	11

SCHUMANN FOR THE CLARINET

1

'You are like a flower'
'Du bist wie eine Blume'

Op.25 No.24

AB 2229

2
A Greeting
Widmung

3
Folksong
Volksliedchen

Op.51 No.2

4
Lotus flower
Die Lotosblume

Fairly slow (in 2)   Op.25 No.7

con Ped.

5
'Ring on my finger'
'Du Ring an meinem Finger'

Andantino

Op.42 No.4

6
'My heart's in the highlands'
Hochländers Abschied

Op.25 No.13

7
Noblest of Men
'Er, der Herrlichste von Allen'

Lively

Op.42 No.2

8
The Two Grenadiers
Die beiden Grenadiere

Moderato alla marcia

Op.49 No.1

9
May Song
'Im wunderschönen Monat Mai'

Slowly, tenderly

Op.48 No.1

segue No.10

10
A Song for Sunday
Sonntag

Moderato

Op.79 No.6

11
Grandee of Spain
Der Hidalgo

With spirit and humour

Op.30 No.3